KT-497-228

Hi, my name is Cameron, *Cammy* for short. I'm here to teach you about the West Coast and Islands of Scotland. I will take you from Oban up through the islands and back down the coast to Oban again, following the arrows on the map shown on the next page. In each place we stop, there will be a puzzle for you to solve. Hope you enjoy the journey. If you get lost just come back to the map to see where you are.

The Scottish people have their own language called *Gaelic*. Here are some of the Gaelic words and phrases that you may see or hear in Scotland and what they mean.

HELLO, HOW ARE YOU? ....Hallo, Ciamar a tha thu

WELCOME ....Fàilte

THANK YOU ....Tapadh leat

GOODBYE ....Tìoraidh

This is a map of the West Coast and Islands of Scotland.

Can you colour in the land one colour and the sea another?

OBAN

Oban is a town in the West Coast of Scotland. Many people visit it every year on holiday. Other people visit Oban to get a ferry to one of the islands off the West Coast from Oban harbour. About 9,000 people live in Oban.

There are lots of things to see when you visit Oban. The ruins of Dunollie Castle can be seen on the hill on the way to the beach at Ganavan. In Oban you can look up the hill in the middle of the town and see McCaig's Tower. It is a round building with no roof and lots of windows. You can walk up there and look down over the houses of Oban into the harbour where the boats are.

Can you draw a picture of what you might see through one of the windows of the tower ?

Ferries leave Oban harbour every day to take people to the islands. In the sea there are different animals. Can you match the animals to their shadows?

Killer Whale

Basking Shark

THE ISLAND OF MULL

The Island of Mull was made a long time ago by a volcano. Its highest point is Ben More (3170 feet) which is known as a munro in Scotland because it is a mountain over 3000 feet high. Nearly 2,500 people live on Mull, many in Tobermory *(Tobar Mhoire - Mary's Well)*. A ferry goes from Oban to Craignure on the Island of Mull. You can walk from the pier to the mini-railway station where a small train will take you to Torosay Castle and Gardens. Torosay Castle is famous for its gardens.

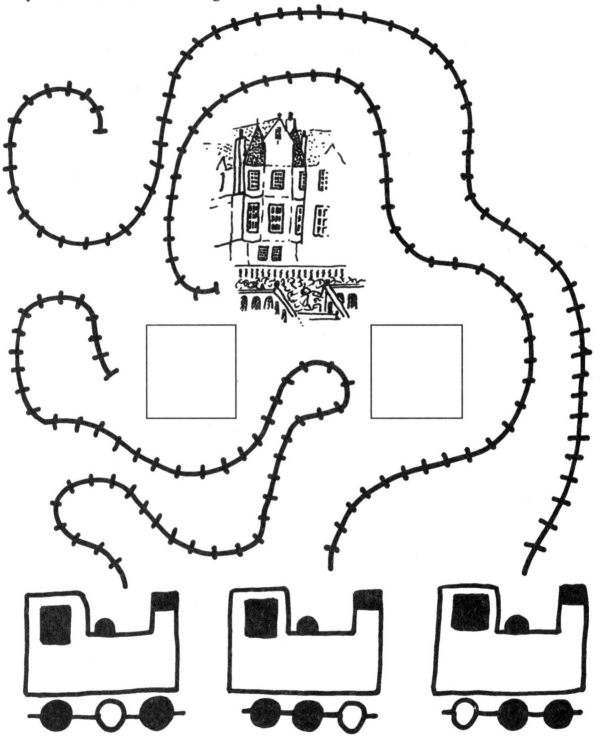

Can you find the train that goes to the castle ?
Can you draw two new flowers for the gardens in the boxes above ?

TOBERMORY

There are many villages on the Island of Mull but Tobermory is the only town. It is well known for its brightly coloured buildings on the main street.

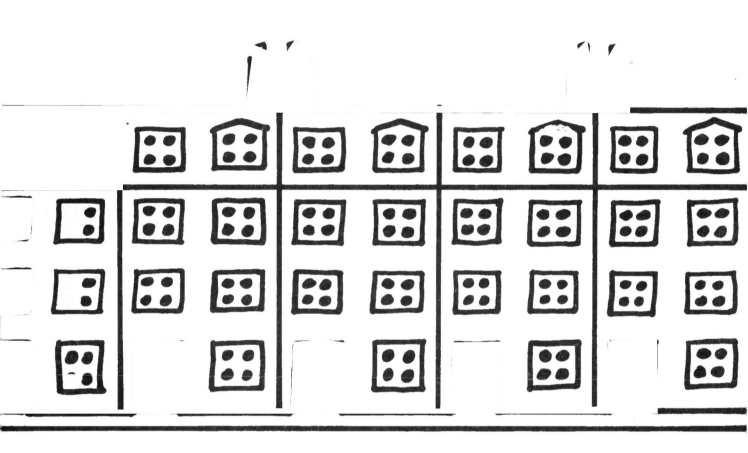

Can you colour in each building a different colour ? Draw your family standing on the main street ?

THE ISLAND OF IONA

The Island of Iona is quite small. It is only 3 ½ miles long and 1 ½ miles wide. Less than 100 people live on the island. Dun- I is the highest point at 332 feet.

People go from the Island of Mull to the Island of Iona on a ferry.

MULL

Can you take the boat to Iona without touching the rocks ?
How many birds can you count in the picture ?

Lots of people visit the Island of Iona. It is special because a man called Saint Columba lived there a long time ago. He came from Ireland in a boat and taught the Scottish people about God.

Iona Abbey was built by Saint Columba many years ago. People still use it to pray and learn about God today.

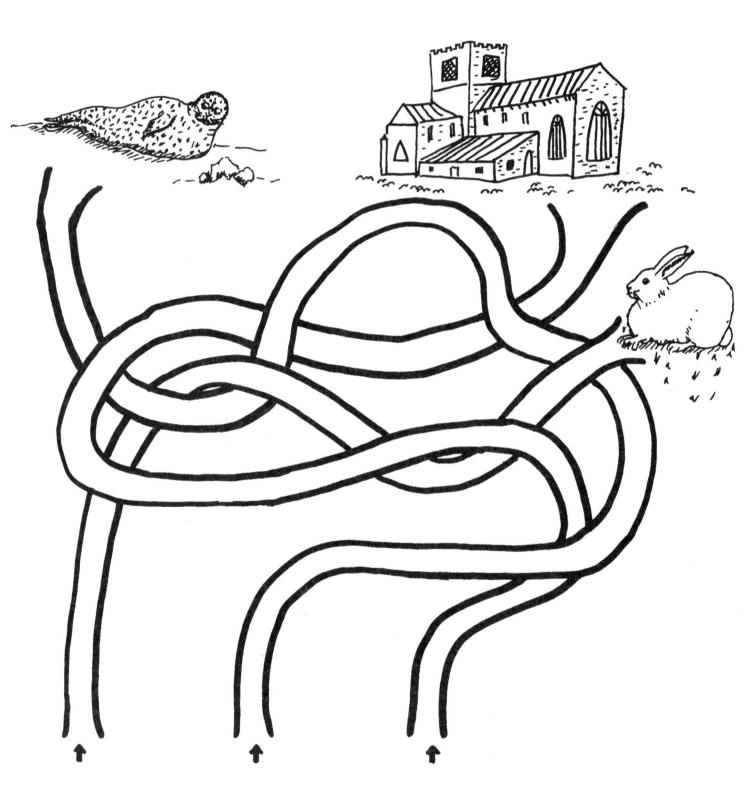

Can you follow the path to find which one takes you to the Abbey ?

THE ISLAND OF STAFFA

The Island of Staffa is a tiny island beside Iona. Staffa is made of columns of basalt caused by volcanic activity; the island is now well known for its caves and birdlife. You can see the hexagonal columns in Fingal's Cave. A famous composer called Mendelssohn wrote music called The Hebrides Overture, after he visited the island in 1829. Today many people visit the island but nobody lives there.

S F I P F U N

The Island of Staffa has lots of birdlife.
Can you colour in all the areas with black dots to find one of the more brightly coloured birds you would find there ? Can you unscramble the letters to name the bird that you find ? _____

THE ISLANDS OF COLL AND TIREE

The Island of Tiree *(Tir-Iodh - the land of corn)* is small. It is a flat island with two high points, Ben Hynish at 462 feet and Ben Hough at 390 feet. About 700 people live on Tiree. The ferry terminal is at Gott Bay next to the main village of Scarnish.

The Island of Coll is also small and flat. Ben Hogh is the highest point at 341 feet. Coll's only village is Arinagour. About 150 people live on the island, half of whom live in the village.

The Islands of Coll and Tiree have beautiful white sandy beaches. There are lots of shells to find on the shores of the island's.

Can you match the shells to the shadows?
Can you colour the shells in ?

Lots of people go wind-surfing in the sea beside Coll and Tiree. Put a different pattern on each sail and colour the picture in.

THE ISLAND OF SKYE

Skye is one of the larger islands. The Cuillin Hills are made up of 20 peaks, 15 of which are munros. The highest mountain is Sgurr Alasdair at 3257 feet. The only town in Skye is Portree *(Port en Righ - Port for the King)* which was named in honour of a visit by King James V in the 16th century. Just over 8,000 people live on Skye.

Can you name some of the villages they may live in and add them to my map?

There are lots of castles on the West Coast and the Islands of Scotland. Many castles like Dunvegan Castle on Skye are owned by Scottish families who are called clans. Dunvegan Castle is owned by the Clan MacLeod. Each clan has its own design for their flag.

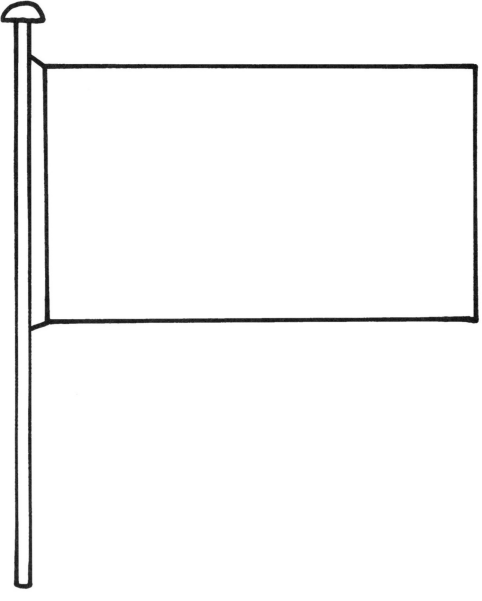

If you owned a castle what would your flag be like ?
Draw it in the space above.

PORTREE

Portree is the main town on Skye. Some of the local fishermen keep their boats in Portree harbour.

Using the shapes can you match the fishing boat to its creel ?

Be careful there are some extra creels that are not for these fishing boats.

How many fish can you find in the picture?

THE CUILLINS OF SKYE

Many people walk or climb in the Cuillin hills on Skye. While they are walking there are lots of animals to see.

Can you join the dots and name the animal that you find?

THE ISLANDS OF NORTH UIST, SOUTH UIST AND BENBECULA

North Uist is an island with lots of salt and freshwater lochs. The highest point is Eaval at 1138 feet. The main village and port for the ferry is Lochmaddy; over 1,600 people live on the island. South Uist is the second largest island in the Outer Hebrides. There are mountains and lots of sandy beaches. The ferry comes into the village of Lochboisdale. About 2,100 people live on South Uist.

The Island of Benbecula *(Beinn a' bhfaodhla - mountain of the fords)* has lots of freshwater lochs. Over 1,600 people live on the island. It is well known because about 250 years ago Bonnie Prince Charlie escaped with Flora MacDonald from Benbecula over the sea to Skye.

In Scotland each family has a Tartan which lets people know which clan they belong to. Tartan is a pattern of colours on cloth. Today you might see the same patterns printed on paper or on presents for people.

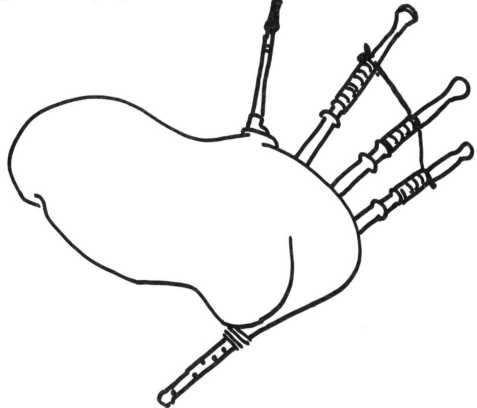

Tartan cloth is used to make part of the most famous Scottish musical instrument - the bagpipes. People enjoy ceilidhs, which are special parties, where there is Scottish music and dancing.

Can you design your own tartan and draw it on the bagpipes above ?

THE ISLAND OF BARRA

About 1,100 people live on the Island of Barra. The highest point is Heaval at 1260 feet. The main village is Castlebay where the ferry comes in.

Built on a rock in Castle Bay on Barra you can visit Kiessimul Castle. It was home for the Clan MacNeil.

Can you draw a castle on the rock below, that you would like to stay in, if you were part of the Clan MacNeil ?

On Barra there are lots of sheep. Their wool is used to make many things.

Can you circle the things which could be made from wool ?

THE ISLANDS OF LEWIS AND HARRIS

There are over 20,000 people living on Lewis. It has two high points; Mealisval at 1885 feet and Beinn Mhor at 1874 feet. Lewis is well known for its peat moor which is scattered with many shallow lochs. Peat is used to burn on fires in peoples' houses to keep them warm and cook their food.

Stornoway, on the Island of Lewis, is the only town in the Outer Hebrides. A lifeboat is based in Stornoway harbour. It is used to help people in danger at sea.

Can you colour in the top part of the lifeboat orange and the bottom part blue ? Your lifeboat will look like every lifeboat in Britain now.

At Callanish on the Island of Lewis there are standing stones.

Which standing stone is the smallest ? Colour it in.

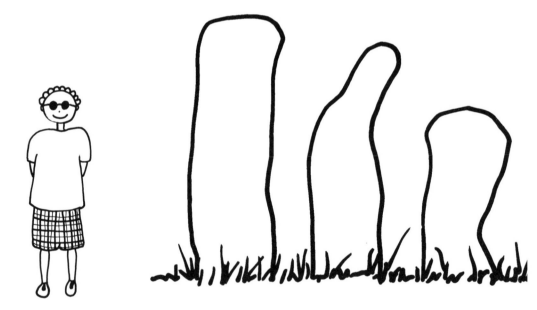

Draw yourself, with me, looking at the standing stones.

The Island of Harris is separated from Lewis by Loch Seaforth, Loch Resort and six miles of high land. The tallest point in the Outer Hebrides is on this land and is called Clisham. It is 2622 feet. Tarbert is the largest village on Harris and it is also where the ferry comes in. About 1,750 people live on the island. It is famous for its tweed cloth. The cloth is made from sheeps wool. There are lots of animals on the Island of Harris. In the picture below rabbits are looking for some carrots.

Can you find three carrots in this picture ? Draw round them.

Can you draw a fluffy tail on each rabbit ? Which two rabbits are the same ?
Colour them in. Colour the other rabbits a different colour.

THE WEST COAST OF SCOTLAND

Time to leave the islands and return to the mainland.

Can you draw a picture of yourself waving goodbye and colour it in?

ULLAPOOL

The ferry from the Outer Hebrides comes in to Ullapool on the mainland. Ullapool is well known as a fishing town. It is on the edge of Loch Broom.

Sometimes people travel around all the sights of the islands and the west coast of Scotland by bus.

How many differences can you see between the pictures shown above?

BRAEMORE

At Braemore you can see Corrieshalloch Gorge. The waterfall that flows through it is called the Falls of Measach. There are lots of waterfalls in Scotland. Here is a picture of a waterfall.

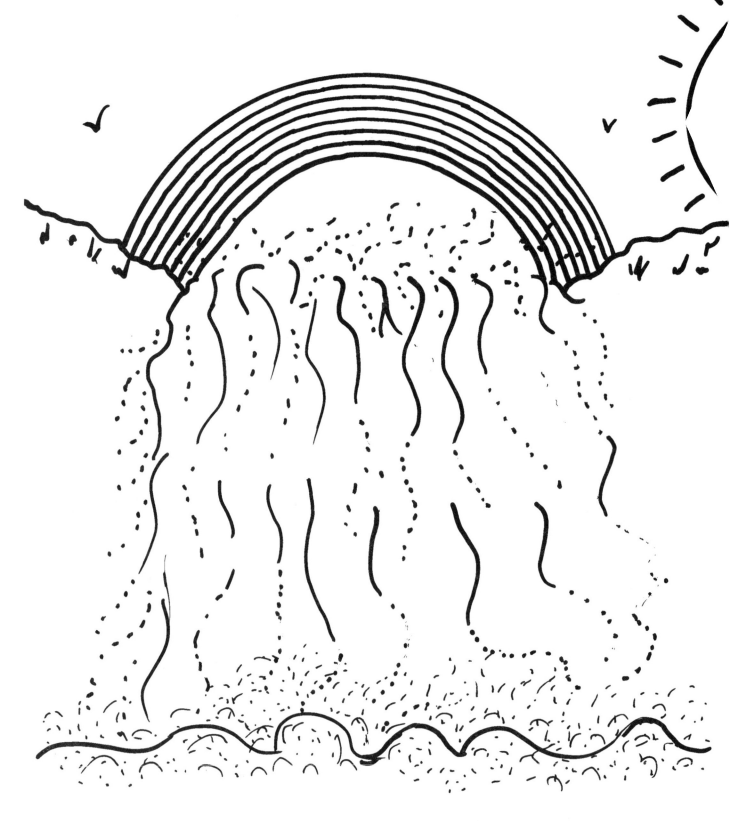

Can you colour in the rainbow at the top and draw some other things you might see where there's a waterfall?

INVEREWE GARDEN

Inverewe Garden is a beautiful highland garden. There are lots of flowers in Scotland, some of them are drawn below. Unscramble the letters to find out which flowers they are .

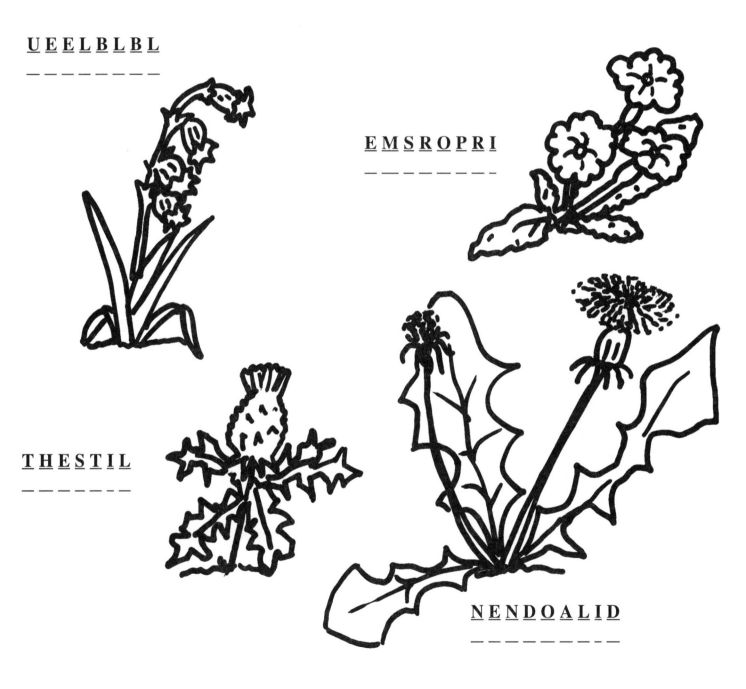

U E E L B L B L

_ _ _ _ _ _ _ _

E M S R O P R I

_ _ _ _ _ _ _ _

T H E S T I L

_ _ _ _ _ _ _

N E N D O A L I D

_ _ _ _ _ _ _ _ _

Do you know which one is known as the 'emblem of Scotland' ?

FORT WILLIAM

Fort William is a town of over 11,000 people, on the edge of Loch Linnhe, the largest sea-water loch in Scotland. Britain's highest mountain at 4406 feet is Ben Nevis which towers above the town. The top of Ben Nevis *(Beinn neamh - bhathais - mountain with its head in the clouds)* is often covered in clouds and this means that Fort William is one of the places in Scotland which gets lots of rain. Luckily there are things to do in the area that don't need good weather.

When I go to Fort William I can go skiing, fishing, hillwalking and Scottish dancing.

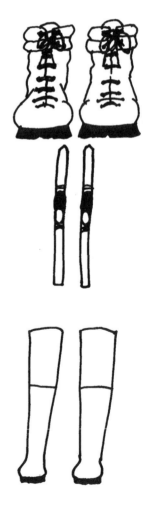

Can you tell me what I should be wearing on my feet for each activity?

In the West Coast and Islands of Scotland, Highland Games are held in the summer. There are lots of different games. Some people do highland dancing, others run races but the sport which needs greatest strength is tossing the caber. The caber is part of a tree trunk and the person who throws it the furthest wins the game.

Can you guess which caber I have tossed ? Which person has tossed the smallest caber ?

Now look at our map on page 4.
That's our journey around the West Coast and Islands of Scotland finished and we're back in Oban. I've had fun, I hope you have too, and I'm sure we'll travel together again soon!
Bye for now, Cammy.

COMPETITION PAGE

A monthly prize will be given for the best drawing or painting. Your drawing or painting should be of something you have seen in, or learnt about Scotland. It should be done on the competition page of this book. The page can be cut out along the dotted line.

Please send your picture along with your name, address and age and the date it was done to:

Cammy's Colouring Competition,
2, The Willows,
Carmunnock,
Glasgow.
G76 9DL.

Rules:
Only one entry per person per month
The entry must be on the competition page provided
Unfortunately no pictures can be returned
Only winning entries will be notified
The decision of the judges' is final.
Details of the winner and the winning entry may form part of Cameron McClure's future publicity.

Also available by Cameron McClure:
Colour - Me - Send - Me Postcards (several designs)
(Soon to be available by *Cameron McClure)*
Puzzle - Me -Teach - Me Activity Books
West Coast and Islands of Scotland Children's Activity Book (Senior)
Scottish Cities & Places Children's Activity Book (Junior)
Scottish Cities & Places Children's Activity Book (Senior)

If you would like more information on any Cameron McClure products please contact:
Cameron McClure,
1 Naseby Avenue,
Glasgow.
G11 7JQ.
Telephone 0141 357 4375
e-mail 101606.3063@compuserve.com

Name:..

Address: ....

....

....

Age: ....

Date Picture Was Done: ....

Please send to:

Cammy's Colouring Competition,
2, The Willows,
Carmunnock,
Glasgow.
G76 9DL.